OOOPS

"The book every girl must have..."

OOOPS!

Chu Chu Onwuachi-Saunders, MD, MPH
Marie Onwuachi, MS, MPH

Illustrated by Lisa M. Green

OOOPS! Publications
Silver Spring, Maryland

Illustrations by Lisa M. Green
Cover Design by Nkechi Ebubedike

Library of Congress Cataloguing-in-Publication Data Available

Library of Congress Control Number 2003095923

ISBN 978-0-9746912-0-6

10 9 8 7 6 5 4 3

Printed in the United States of America
Third Edition

For
Our Princesses: Nkechi, Ayana, Imade, Nneka,
Ife, Isoken, and Mowa

Kehinde and Taiwo are eleven-year-old identical twins in every sense of the word except for one thing: Kehinde, who insisted everyone call her Kenny, was born second and always tried her very best to be different from her twin sister. The thought of being just like her twin annoyed Kenny. If Taiwo said she liked cats, Kenny would say she liked dogs better, even though she really liked cats, way more than her sister. If Taiwo said she liked chocolate ice cream, Kenny would say she liked vanilla, even though watching Taiwo eat chocolate ice cream made her mouth water.

One day, something very different happened to both of the girls at the same time.

"OOOPS!" exclaimed Taiwo. She had just woken up and felt wetness in her underwear. Looking under the covers, she found her underwear stained with blood.

"Kenny, guess what! I think my period started," she said, joyfully.

Kenny rolled her eyes at Taiwo.

"So what, I have too. But why are you so excited? You know it means that we'll have to cancel our plans to go out tomorrow," said Kenny.

"Why?" asked Taiwo.

"Because having our period means we can't do anything like we used to," said Kenny, pulling the covers up over her head.

"I don't believe you," said Taiwo. "I'm going to talk to Nana." She jumped out of bed and ran to her grandmother's room. "Nana, Nana, guess what? Kenny and I have started our periods – I think." Taiwo wrinkled her nose, unsure of what she was saying.

"What do you mean 'you think,' young lady?" Nana asked, with a big smile on her face.

Taiwo began asking her a string of questions all at once. "Nana, does this mean we can't go to the dance? Are we going to get cramps, PMS or something? Can we take a bath?"

"Wait a minute, wait one second," said Nana. "Who told you all of this nonsense?"

"Kenny said our plans for tomorrow are ruined because we have started our periods," said Taiwo. "But I don't care. I feel great, like I'm special. Is this how I am suppose to feel, Nana?"

"Well, I hate it," said Kenny as she entered the room plopping down on the foot of Nana's bed.

"Nana, tell her what having your period really does to girls, how it ruins our lives every month."

"I will tell you all about what having your period does to girls, but it certainly won't be anything that will ruin your life, Kenny. But before I tell anyone anything, the two of you should go and have a warm bath and get cleaned up," said Nana.

"A bath?" cried Kenny. "I thought you couldn't have a bath while you are on your period. The girls at school say-"

"Never mind what the girls at school say," Nana interrupted. "Just go and take a bath, and don't forget to put on a sanitary pad just like I showed you before. It is very important to keep

clean, especially during this time. You will feel better. When you come back we'll talk some more about what having your period is really all about."

Kenny and Taiwo went and took a bath.

"Oh, I feel clean, and smell good," said Taiwo, as she dried herself with a towel.

"Well, I don't feel any different," said Kenny, even though she felt much better, maybe even better than Taiwo. But she'd never say so, because she didn't want to be just like her twin.

The girls got dressed and went downstairs. They found Nana sitting in her rocking chair next to their favorite window seat.

"Come, my sweethearts, sit down and let me tell you all about this wonderful change that has happened to you," she said. "By the way, don't you feel better, now that you've had a bath?" Taiwo smiled and nodded her head with delight, while Kenny just looked down with her arms crossed.

"You know Kenny, you remind me of your mother when she first started her period," said Nana smiling. "She heard the same stories from her friends and disliked being on her period."

"What did you tell her?" asked Kenny, a smile coming to her face for the first time that day. Kenny loved to hear stories about their mother, who was often away with their father on archeological digs in faraway countries like Egypt and Turkey. Whenever they are off on a dig Nana is always in charge. She has been living with them since Kenny and Taiwo were born.

"First of all, I told her that long ago in many places, when a girl was having her period, this was considered a special time for her," said

Nana. "During this time, she was usually relieved of all her chores. This gave her time alone to take care of herself and feel special like a princess."

"A princess? I knew I felt different for some reason," said Taiwo.

"Taiwo, tell the truth, you know you feel dirty, ashamed and like a wet duck,

just like everybody else," said Kenny.

"Now Kenny, please don't talk like that. I know that your period feels different, but after awhile, you will get used to having it every month and feel better about it, too," said Nana.

"But Nana, there are so many things we can't do anymore," cried Kenny. "I almost wish I was a boy!"

"Kenny, you can still do whatever you want when you are on your period," said Nana, winking at Taiwo. "And you will even find you are more creative during your period, so you can use this time to focus and do something special. You should also get plenty of rest and eat healthy. Since we women are always taking care of everyone else, our period acts like an internal automatic clock to remind us to stop, and take

care of ourselves. Do something kind for yourself every time your period arrives. Pamper yourself. Practice this now, because as you become older you will have more to do and might forget to take care of the most important person . . . 'u'."

Then Nana leaned forward in her chair and said very calmly: "But remember, whether a girl is on her period or not, she should always respect her body, love it, cherish it, and never do anything to harm it."

That night, just before going to sleep, Kenny and Taiwo were talking about what Nana had told them earlier that day about their periods.

"Kenny, guess what? I've decided to start writing in my journal twice a day during my period," said Taiwo.

"Twice, why?" asked Kenny.

"Don't you remember? Nana said we are creative and should pamper ourselves during our periods. You know I like writing in my journal. It helps me to express my feelings and then I feel better. What are you going to do?" asked Taiwo, yawning.

"I don't know. I do know one thing: I don't want to remember my period," said Kenny. Kenny secretly wanted to write in her journal also. She wanted to write down everything that was happening to her and her body, especially now. But she'd never say so, because she just didn't want to be like her twin.

The next day at school, Taiwo ran into her friend Ayana and told her the good news.

"Guess what Ayana, I became a woman yesterday," said Taiwo, happily.

"Did you start your period?" Ayana whispered.

"Yes, and I feel like a princess," said Taiwo, proudly.

"Shhh! You don't want the boys to hear you.

They aren't supposed to know, and besides, you're not a woman. You're still a girl," said Ayana.

"Hmmm, you're right," said Taiwo. "But it doesn't matter who knows, as long as I know that I'm special."

"Who told you that?" asked Ayana, curiously.

"My Nana. She said that long ago, women and girls always felt special when they were on their periods. That's the way it should be now, and we have got to start reminding each other. Nana also said that this is the time when you should do something special for 'u'." That this is the time when girls are very creative, and we should try different, new and special things," said Taiwo, matter-of-factly. "Ayana, you know how you love hip hop so much, well, maybe you should try writing a song of your own when you are on your period."

"Now, that's an idea," said Ayana.

"Being on your period is all that," said Taiwo, smiling.

"Well, if it's all that, then you figure out how we're going to have a good time this evening at the dance," said Kenny, as she walked up to join the girls. "I don't want to have to change my pad at the dance, and what if I stain my new jeans? How embarrassing."

"Being on your period is special, so you shouldn't be embarrassed about anything," said Ayana, grinning as she looked at Taiwo. "And everybody stains their clothes once in awhile, Kenny. It's a normal part of having your period. Believe me, I know," said Ayana, wrinkling her nose.

"Yeah, Kenny, she's right. I won't feel ashamed to change my pads as many times as I need to," said Taiwo. "Remember, Nana said that if we change pads more often we will feel better. If we feel better about being on our periods, then we won't be embarrassed anymore. You did remember to bring your OOOPS! pack that Nana gave us, didn't you Kenny?" asked Taiwo.

" What's an OOOPS! pack?" asked Ayana. "It's just a pretty pouch with a sanitary pad, some towelettes, and a pair of underwear in it," said Taiwo. "It's great! Come on, let's go change now."

Taiwo grabbed her sister by the hand and the three of them went into the girls' bathroom. After changing, the twins came out of the stalls with their used pads wrapped and ready to be thrown away.

"Ugh, I hate having to carry that nasty thing," said Kenny, as she watched Taiwo walk over to the trashcan and toss her wrapped pad in with a smile on her face.

"You know what? I feel better already," said Taiwo, while she and Kenny washed their hands. Kenny secretly felt better too, but she didn't say a word.

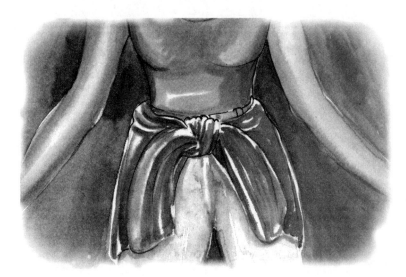

"Don't forget to bring your sweaters with you to the dance," said Ayana. "I'll show you how to tie it around your waist so that if you do get stained, you will still look good."

"Now that's an idea," said Kenny. She was beginning to feel better about being on her period.

That evening at the dance, Taiwo, Kenny and Ayana sat with some of their friends and began talking about being on their periods.

"My Nana also said that girls should treat themselves like princesses during their periods," said Taiwo.

"Well, that's fair enough, considering it's only 12 times a year," joked Justin, after overhearing the girls. Kenny really liked Justin.

To her, he was the cutest and smartest boy in the entire school, and she liked him even more because her sister Taiwo didn't.

"Very funny, Justin," said Taiwo, rolling her eyes.

"Whether you guys like it or not, we will be acting like princesses every month," said Kenny, while looking at Justin.

"I would be happy to treat you like a princess everyday, Kenny," said Justin as he handed her a rose and sat down beside her.

The next moment Kenny felt something. She was beginning to feel like a "wet duck." Her pad was leaking right now in front of all these people, including Justin. Thank goodness she had thrown her OOOPS! pack in her bag, after a last-minute warning from her sister. But how was she going to make an exit without everyone knowing where she was going, and what she was going to do. Then a thought came to her: "I am a princess and a princess always keeps her cool because she believes in herself."

Kenny slowly moved her sweater, from her shoulders down to her waist, and tied it into a knot. Again, thanks to Taiwo, she was wearing her new red sweater instead of her favorite old blue one. She waited for her moment, took a deep breath, and with a very calm voice announced, "Excuse me, I'm going to the ladies room to make sure I am still beautiful before we get this party started. Anybody else want to go?" Ayana and Taiwo jumped up and followed Kenny, almost tripping over each other. Of course, they wanted to make sure they were still beautiful too.

This OOOPS! pack is a lifesaver, thought Kenny as she tossed her wrapped used pad into the trashcan. Because her OOOPS! pack had a change of underwear in it, she really felt better although her new jeans were slightly stained. She decided she would keep the sweater around her waist anyway. It actually looked good.

Kenny smiled as she washed her hands and looked at her reflection in the mirror. She really looked beautiful. This was going to be great, especially if Justin was going to treat her like a princess. And now she really felt like a princess after pulling off that smart move. Not even Taiwo knew what she had just done. She would tell her just before they went to bed so she could see the look on her face.

Suddenly she didn't feel embarrassed or annoyed anymore. In fact, pampering herself every month was going to take getting used to, but she would enjoy it, and was convinced she deserved it. And for the first time ever, she felt good about liking something her sister liked, being on her period.

.............to be continued

Monthly Stickers

Use the following calendars
to track your period for a year.
Each month place an OOOPS! sticker
on the days you have your period.
Remember to record what you did
to pamper yourself and write in your journal.
Have fun!

Visit us at www.theooopsbook.com
to order additional copies of the book,
chat about the book,
and learn more about
the OOOPS! Pac for U

Month: **Year:**

Sun	Mon	Tue	Wed	Thu	Fri	Sat

What one thing did I do special for myself during this OOOPS! ?

Month: **Year:**

Sun	Mon	Tue	Wed	Thu	Fri	Sat

What one thing did I do special for myself during this OOOPS! ?

Month: **Year:**

Sun	Mon	Tue	Wed	Thu	Fri	Sat

OOOPS

What one thing did I do special for myself during this OOOPS! ?

Month: **Year:**

Sun	Mon	Tue	Wed	Thu	Fri	Sat

What one thing did I do special for myself during this OOOPS! ?

month: **Year:**

Sun	mon	Tue	Wed	Thu	Fri	Sat

OOOPS

What one thing did I do special for myself during this OOOPS! ?

Month: **Year:**

Sun	Mon	Tue	Wed	Thu	Fri	Sat

What one thing did I do special for myself during this OOOPS! ?

Month: **Year:**

Sun	Mon	Tue	Wed	Thu	Fri	Sat

What one thing did I do special for myself during this OOOPS! ?

Month: **Year:**

Sun	Mon	Tue	Wed	Thu	Fri	Sat

What one thing did I do special for myself during this OOOPS! ?

Month: **Year:**

Sun	Mon	Tue	Wed	Thu	Fri	Sat

OOOPS

What one thing did I do special for myself during this OOOPS!?

Month: Year:

Sun	Mon	Tue	Wed	Thu	Fri	Sat

What one thing did I do special for myself during this MONTH ?

Month: **Year:**

Sun	Mon	Tue	Wed	Thu	Fri	Sat

What one thing did I do special for myself during this OOOPS! ?

Month: **Year:**

Sun	Mon	Tue	Wed	Thu	Fri	Sat

What one thing did I do special for myself during this OOOPS! ?

My Journal

My Journal

My Journal

My Journal

My Journal

My Journal

My Journal

My Journal

My Journal

My Journal

My Journal

My Journal

My Journal

My Journal

My Journal

My Journal

About the Authors

Chu Chu Onwuachi-Saunders, MD, MPH is a pediatrician and former medical epidemiologist with the U.S. Centers for Disease Control and Prevention (CDC) where for over 10 years she was involved with issues related to children's health. She was also a reproductive health program officer at the Ford Foundation, and is currently a professor, public health consultant, highly sought after public speaker and the mother of two, Ayana and Shakir.

Marie Onwuachi, MS, MPH is a public health consultant, film producer and entrepreneur with over 20 years of experience working with youth and families. She is also the mother of two daughters.

About the Illustrators

Lisa M. Green was encouraged by her family at an early age to paint and draw. She has a Bachelor of Fine Arts from the Pratt Institute and a Masters of Art as Applied to Medicine from the Johns Hopkins School of Medicine. She creates with various mediums and her work is exhibited throughout the Washington, DC metropolitan area.

Nkechi Ebubedike graduated from Carnegie Mellon University with a major in fine arts. This is her first book cover design and she really enjoyed working on it because it reminded her of her first OOOPS!

OOOPS! Glossary

Cramps: Pain or discomfort felt by some girls when the uterus muscle contracts during the period.

Pamper: To do something special for yourself that makes you feel happy. (e.g. listening to your favorite music, taking a soothing bath, reading a good book).

Period: The word used for the monthly normal flow of blood and tissue from the inside of the uterus to the outside of the body.

Pre-Menstrual Syndrome (PMS): A group of unusual feelings (e.g. moodiness) or physical changes (e.g. weight gain, breast tenderness) that occur one or two weeks before the period comes.

Princess: The daughter of a king and queen, but in this book it's you - a beautiful young lady who is happy, believes in herself and knows that she has the power to make her dreams come true.

Uterus: The pear shaped organ in the body of a female where a baby grows and is protected before it is born.